When I'm Surprised

Moira Butterfield

WAYLAND

First published in 2014 by Wayland
© Wayland 2014

Wayland
Hachette Children's Books
338 Euston Road
London NW1 3BH

Wayland Australia
Level 17/207 Kent Street
Sydney NSW 2000

Produced for Wayland by
White-Thomson Publishing Ltd
www.wtpub.co.uk
+44 (0) 843 208 7460

Editor: Stephen White-Thomson
Design: Rocket Design (East Anglia) Ltd

A catalogue for this title is available from the British Library

ISBN: 9780750282833
e-book ISBN: 9780750291231

Dewey Number: 152.4-dc23

10 9 8 7 6 5 4 3 2 1

Wayland is a division of Hachette Children's Books,
an Hachette UK company.
www.hachette.co.uk

Printed and bound in China

Picture credits:
Shutterstock.com: maxim ibragimov 3, Valua Vitaly 4, Gelpi JM 5, 6, 22,
Christophe Testi 8, 22, Mike Degteariov 9, Jenn Huls 10, Nanette Grebe 11,
22, dotshock 12, AJP 13, 2xSamara.com 14, 20, Luis Louro 15, karelnoppe 16,
Suzanne Tucker 17, Samuel Borges Photography 18, 22, Monkey Business
Images 19, Denys Prykhodov 21, Thinkstock/LUNAMARINA 7, 22

Sometimes you might have...

a bad surprise...

a good surprise...

or a surprise that feels so big...

...it feels as if you've been turned upside down...

Take a look and see...

We don't like **bad surprises.**

They make us feel **rotten!**

splat!

splat!

splat!

5

A good surprise
might be
**getting a
present...**

WOW!

6

A bad surprise might be a loud noise that **makes you jump...**

POP!

8

...or being really kind
to someone.

You look great today!

Some surprises are **really big**. They are like a **whirly wind** that rushes in, bringing lots of feelings...

...like finding out you are moving house...

...or hearing that you are moving schools.

14

A whirly wind surprise can make you feel as if you've been turned

upside-down.

15

It can fill your head **with worries.**

Will things be worse?

Will things go wrong?

You might start to imagine all the **bad things** that could happen.

There's a way to calm a whirly wind surprise
Instead of the bad things...

...think of the **good** **things** the surprise might bring.

If you move house, you will have a new bedroom.

It could turn out to be the

best bedroom ever!

BOUNCE!
BOUNCE!

19

If you move school you will meet new friends. There's a lot of fun to look forward to!

Do it!

Pretend to get a **surprise present.**

Pretend to give someone a **surprise present.**

Pretend to see a **surprise rainbow.**

Pretend to find a **spider in the bath.**

Pretend to **jump** with surprise.

Say something **nice** to someone.

Imagine a whirly wind is **blowing over you.**

Imagine calming the **whirly wind.**

Teacher's and parent's notes:

These books are designed for children to explore feelings in a fun interactive way. Encourage them to have fun pointing to the pictures, making sounds and doing some acting, too.

During or after your reading, you could encourage your child to talk further about their own feelings, if they want to. Here are some conversation prompts to try:

Describe how you feel when you get a good surprise or a bad surprise.

Can you think of a good surprise that you would like to happen to you?

Activities to try:

✳ Make a list of nice surprises you could give people that you know. For instance, you could paint a picture or write a poem and give it to them.

✳ On a piece of paper, draw your favourite picture from this book.

Further reading:

I'm Worried,
written by Brian Moses and illustrated by Mike Gordon (Wayland)

William Worrydactyl,
written by Brian Moses and illustrated by Mike Gordon (Wayland, 2013)